Use these stickers to complete the story.

Pages 2-3

Pages 4-5

Pages 6-7

Pages 8-9

Pages 10-11

Pages 12-13

Pages 14-15

Page 16

Christmas Is Coming!

By Carolee Brockmann
Illustrated by Nan Brooks

LITTLE SIMON
An imprint of Simon & Schuster Children's Publishing Division
1230 Avenue of the Americas, New York, New York 10020
Created and manufactured by arrangement with Ottenheimer Publishers, Inc.
Copyright © 1998 by Ottenheimer Publishers, Inc.
Manufactured in the United States of America
10 9 8 7 6 5 4 3 2 1
ISBN 0-689-81806-8
SF855A

Christmas is coming! I'll tell you how I know!

Big come down from the attic

and Mom hangs the !

Jack unwinds green while I unwrap the

to put near our small wooden

where baby Jesus sleeps.

and ! A wreath goes on the door.

What does baby Lisa have?

Oops! Tinsel—all over the floor.

2

STICKER WORDS

garlands
mistletoe
Nutcrackers
sheep
stable
boxes
Santa hats

STICKER WORDS

angel
dove
bulbs
lights
evergreen
reindeer

Christmas is coming! Dad puts up an  .

The piney smell fills us with memories

of snowy Christmas scenes.

Dad tests the —hooray! They all work this year.

I unwrap Mom's favorite bells.

Lisa hangs up a tiny .

Here are eight frosted of ruby-red glass,

and the paper-plate

from my preschool class!

Christmas is really coming! My  gives me the clue—

there's  in the kitchen

and Mom's Christmas cookies, too!

Dad keeps nibbling  ; he says that it was  .

My gingerbread walls keep falling down!

"Someone, please help me put them back!"

Mom mixes some extra icing to help the walls to stick.

We squeeze out rows of red and green.

"There! That should do the trick!"

STICKER WORDS

Jack
gingerbread
nose
cookies

STICKER WORDS

sweater
tape
pen
present

Christmas is finally coming! It's  -wrapping time.

"Jack, don't look while I wrap yours!"

(I peek while he wraps mine.)

Lisa's in trouble. She's not very good with  .

But she's great at *unwrapping* presents.

Grab her! Oops! Too late!

She's putting on Grandma's new  ! She's unwrapping

Grandpa's new  !

When Jack and I stop laughing,

we'll wrap them up again.

Christmas at last is coming. I hear the doorbell ring.

My uncle and aunt bring

and we gather round to sing.

As Aunt Lil plays , she hums a Christmas song.

Uncle Arthur knows all the words.

Our dog barks along.

We sing "Joy to the " and "Deck the Halls."

We laugh through "Jingle "

while night begins to fall.

STICKER WORDS

Skipper
piano
Bells
World
fruitcake

11

Christmas is tomorrow! Our hang in a line.

Jack hopes to get a ,

but a would be fine.

I'd like to get a , or a musical .

Jack says kids used to get .

"Be good," I tease, "or you'll get rocks!"

Lisa says she wants a toy. That's really nothing new.

We give her a hug and ask her,

"What *kind* of toy?" She says, "Blue!"

STICKER WORDS

oranges
toy pony
jewelry box
stockings
paint set
gum-ball machine

Christmas Eve is almost over. The  shine on the .

Mom reads *The Night Before Christmas*

to Dad, Jack, Lisa, and me.

Then she reads from the Bible about the wondrous ,

and how the and

brought from afar.

We leave cookies and for Santa's midnight snack.

Daddy tries to sneak one,

then winks and puts it back.

STICKER WORDS

shepherds
star
presents
milk
wise men
lights
tree

15

Seven more hours till Christmas! We listen for sounds—

the prancing and pawing of each tiny

as makes his rounds.

We should dream of , but we dance around instead.

Dad says, "Quiet down up there!"

"Get back into your !"

Santa Claus is coming, bringing more Christmas cheer.

We're ready for Christmas at our ,

and soon it will be here!

STICKER WORDS

house
Santa
hoof
beds
sugarplums
reindeer

Here's an extra set of stickers! Use them to create your own rebus sentences or to decorate your holiday cards and packages.